SLIM & TRIM
COOKBOOK

SUE ASHWORTH

SIMON & SCHUSTER

LONDON·SYDNEY·NEW·YORK·TOKYO·SINGAPORE·TORONTO

First published in Great Britain by Simon & Schuster, 1995
A Paramount Communications Company

Copyright ©1995, Weight Watchers (UK) Ltd

Simon & Schuster Ltd
West Garden Place
Kendal Street
London W2 2AQ

Design: Green Moore Lowenhoff
Typesetting: Stylize
Photography: Iain Bagwell
Styling: Rachel Jukes
Food preparation: Sue Ashworth

Weight Watchers Publications Manager: Delia Bintley
Weight Watchers Publications Assistant: Celia Whiston

A CIP catalogue record is available from the British Library

ISBN 0-671-71414-7

Printed and bound in the United Kingdom by Print Wright Limited, Ipswich

Pictured on the front cover: *Sweet and Sour Beef and Peppers (page 40)*

Recipe notes:
Egg size is medium (size 3), unless otherwise stated.
Vegetables are medium-size, unless otherwise stated.
It is important to use proper measuring spoons, not cutlery, for
spoon measures.
1 tablespoon = 15 ml; 1 teaspoon = 5 ml.
Dried herbs can be substituted for fresh ones, but the flavour will not
always be so good. Halve the fresh-herb quantity stated in the recipe.

Vegetarian recipes:
These symbols show which recipes are suitable for vegetarians.

(V) shows the recipe is vegetarian

(V) shows the recipe has a vegetarian option

The Slim and Trim Programme for men and young people:
The recipes in this book have been designed to fit the Slim and Trim
daily Selection totals for women. The Selections remaining per day
are those for women. On the Slim and Trim Programme men and
young people aged between 10 and 16 should eat additional
Carbohydrate, Fruit, Milk and Protein Selections. Some recipes
indicate options for men and young people. Full details of the Food
Plan can be found within the Programme Material.

Contents

Introduction

Small, but beautiful – that's the new Weight Watchers *Slim and Trim Cookbook*. Small, with just 30 recipes in it, making it easy to find a recipe that fits into your new healthy-eating regime. Beautiful, because the recipes are simple, quick and practical and – best of all – delicious.

We at Weight Watchers don't believe in suffering to get slim. Perseverance, commitment and determination, yes, those are words that many Members of the world's most successful slimming organisation can relate to. But suffering – definitely not! This book will help you create interesting, satisfying food for you and your family. If you are a new Member, you will find it fits in perfectly with the new healthy way of eating you are learning about. If you are a long-standing Weight Watchers Member who knows the Programme inside-out, it will give you new ideas and inspiration to add variety to your everyday meals.

On the Slim and Trim Programme you eat three meals a day: Breakfast, a Light Meal and a Main Meal; all the recipes in this book have been designed with this in mind. Selections are given for each recipe, and you will find that they fall within the guidelines for each type of meal. In most cases, you will not have to use all the Selections available (profiles can be found within the Programme Material), so you can still choose to supplement the meals, perhaps adding a piece of fruit with Breakfast, or extra protein with your Light Meal. You will also see that most Light and Main Meal recipes do not make full use of the fruit allowance: women can eat one Fruit Selection with each meal. If no Fruit Selection is shown you should choose one from the Fruit Section of your Food Lists and either have it as part of your meal or as a snack during the day.

To make planning your day even easier, as well as telling you what Selections you have used up, we also list the Selections you still have available. So, browse through the recipes in the *Slim and Trim Cookbook* and start by trying out two or three. You'll quickly discover – like thousands of Members before you – that not only is the food on the Weight Watchers Programme more healthy, it's more delicious too.

Breakfasts

Everyone knows that it's a good idea to have a proper breakfast, but, let's face it, who listens to this sound advice? Often, because of other pressures at such a busy time of the day, we skip breakfast, thinking that we'll be saving both time and Calories! Try to slow down, catch your breath, and make a little time for yourself each morning. Not only will you be setting yourself up for the busy day ahead by feeling calmer and more prepared, but you'll be setting your body up too. After all, you do need literally to break your fast – you've not eaten since the previous evening. It may mean that you have to prise yourself out of bed a little earlier, but it's in a very good cause.

In this chapter of breakfast ideas, you'll find a quick and easy recipe for home-made muesli, which is better than shop-bought varieties because you know exactly what you have put into it. Make up a quantity and it will last for several days. There are also a couple of tasty ideas for cooked breakfasts, and a delicious recipe for a fruit compote that can be eaten warm or cold. It really does make sense to eat breakfast when you are dieting because breakfast keeps hunger pangs at bay until lunchtime, and protects you from those moments of weakness that occur around mid-morning. Besides, with breakfasts like these, who wants to stay in bed?

Mighty Mushrooms on Toast

Start your day with a delicious cooked breakfast that takes only minutes to make. It will keep the hunger pangs at bay – at least until lunchtime.

Serves: 1
Calories per serving: 145
Preparation and cooking time: 15 minutes
Freezing: not recommended
Selections per serving: 1 Carbohydrate; 1/2 Fat;
    1 Vegetable; 15 Optional Calories
Selections remaining per day: 3–5 Carbohydrate;
    1 1/2–2 1/2 Fat; 2–3 Fruit; 2 Milk; 3–6 Protein;
    2 Vegetable

4 oz (120 g) mushrooms, wiped and sliced
1/4 pint (150 ml) stock, made with 1/2 vegetable
    stock cube
1 oz (30 g) slice of whole-grain bread
1 teaspoon low-fat spread
1/2 teaspoon Marmite
1 teaspoon cornflour, mixed to a paste with a little
    cold water

❶ Put the mushrooms and vegetable stock in a small saucepan and heat until just boiling. Reduce the heat and simmer gently for five minutes.

❷ Meanwhile, toast the bread and spread with the low-fat spread and Marmite. Put on a warm serving plate.

❸ Lift the mushrooms on to the toast with a draining spoon, reserving the cooking liquid. Add the cornflour paste to the cooking liquid, stirring to blend. Heat until the sauce is thickened and smooth. Pour the sauce over the mushrooms and serve immediately.

Variations: to make Creamy Mushrooms on Toast, replace the vegetable stock with skimmed milk from your daily allowance and omit the Marmite. This reduces the Optional Calories to 10.

You can use this recipe as the basis of a Light Meal, using 1 oz (30 g) pitta instead of toast, if you prefer. Warm the pitta bread first, and stuff it with some shredded lettuce before spooning in the mushrooms.

Tomato Herb Omelette

Make a satisfying omelette, packed full of sliced tomatoes and flavoured with snipped fresh herbs, for a bright start to your day.

Serves: 1
Calories per serving: 140
Preparation and cooking time: 10 minutes
Freezing: not recommended
Selections per serving: 1/2 Fat; 1 Protein;
   1 Vegetable; 10 Optional Calories
Selections remaining per day: 4–6 Carbohydrate;
   1 1/2–2 1/2 Fat; 2–3 Fruit; 2 Milk; 3–6 Protein;
   2 Vegetable

Ⓥ if using free-range egg and vegetarian margarine

1 egg
2 tablespoons skimmed milk
1 teaspoon chopped fresh herbs, e.g., chives,
   parsley, basil or oregano, or 1/2 teaspoon
   dried herbs
1/2 teaspoon margarine or olive oil
2 tomatoes, sliced thinly
salt and pepper
1 oz (30 g) bread roll, to serve

❶ Beat the egg and milk together and season with a little salt and pepper. Add the chopped herbs and mix together.

❷ Heat the margarine or olive oil in a small frying-pan. Preheat the grill.

❸ Pour the egg mixture into the pan and cook over a medium-high heat for about two minutes to set the base. Lay the tomato slices over one half of the omelette and season them with salt and pepper.

❹ Cook the surface of the omelette under the grill until lightly set.

❺ Fold the omelette over the tomatoes and serve at once with the bread roll.

Variations: trim and finely chop 2 spring onions and lightly sauté them in the margarine or oil, before adding the egg.

Use 3 oz (90 g) sliced mushrooms, instead of tomatoes, for a change.

Make a simple but tasty fresh herb omelette by using two or three different types of herbs: use 2 teaspoons of chopped fresh herbs altogether. Basil, oregano and parsley is a delicious combination. This removes the Vegetable Selection.

Previous page: Mighty Mushrooms on Toast
Tomato Herb Omelette

Spiced Breakfast Fruits

Fresh apples, pears and plums are gently simmered in apple juice and flavoured with cinnamon in this refreshing breakfast compote. Serve each portion topped with a spoonful of low-fat natural yogurt.

Serves: 4

Preparation and cooking time: 15 minutes

Calories per serving: 70

Freezing: not recommended

Selections per serving: 1 Fruit; 10 Optional Calories

Selections remaining per day: 4–6 Carbohydrate; 2–3 Fat; 1–2 Fruit; 2 Milk; 3–6 Protein; 3 Vegetable

1 medium-size apple

1 medium-size pear

4 oz (120 g) plums

4 fl oz (120 ml) unsweetened apple or grape juice

1 tablespoon lemon juice

2 fl oz (60 ml) water

$1/2$ teaspoon ground cinnamon or $1/2$ cinnamon stick

artificial sweetener, to taste

4 tablespoons low-fat natural yogurt, to serve

❶ Core and slice the apple and pear. Halve the plums and remove the stones; then cut them into quarters.

❷ Put all the fruit with the apple or grape juice, lemon juice and water in a small saucepan. Add the ground cinnamon or cinnamon stick. Simmer gently for 8–10 minutes, until the fruit is tender. Cool slightly. Remove the cinnamon stick, if used.

❸ Serve one quarter of the fruit per portion, with a little artificial sweetener to taste. Top each serving with 1 tablespoon of low-fat natural yogurt.

❹ Any leftover compote can be refrigerated, covered, for 4–5 days.

Variations: substitute one of the following for the apple, pear or plums: 1 oz (30 g) dried prunes or dates, chopped; or 2 oz (60 g) fresh figs, sliced; or 4 oz (120 g) fresh apricots, halved, stoned and quartered; or 1 medium-size orange, segmented (add it to the other fruits after they have cooked).

Weight Watchers note: Members following the Slim and Trim Programme should add 1 Carbohydrate Selection to complete their meal (see your Food Lists for suitable choices). Remember to deduct 1 Carbohydrate from your Selections remaining per day.

Breakfast Muesli

Make up a quantity of your own muesli, following this tasty and nutritious recipe. Each morning you can weigh yourself a portion, and then vary it by adding some fruit from your daily allowance.

Makes: 10 × 1 oz (30 g) servings
Calories per serving: 125
Preparation and cooking time: 15 minutes
Freezing: not recommended
Selections per serving: 1 Carbohydrate;
   10 Optional Calories
Selections remaining per day: 3–5 Carbohydrate;
   2–3 Fat; 2–3 Fruit; 2 Milk; 3–6 Protein;
   3 Vegetable

4 oz (120 g) porridge oats
3 teaspoons unsalted sunflower seeds
4 oz (120 g) unsweetened wheatflakes, branflakes
   or cornflakes
2 oz (60 g) wheatgerm
¹/₂ oz (15 g) blanched almonds, chopped

❶ Preheat the grill to medium-hot. Scatter the porridge oats and sunflower seeds on to a baking sheet. Grill them for about 5 minutes until lightly toasted, and then allow them to cool.
❷ Lightly crush the wheatflakes, branflakes or cornflakes and add the wheatgerm, almonds and toasted porridge oats and sunflower seeds. Mix together well.
❸ Transfer the muesli to an airtight container. Weigh out 1 oz (30 g) for one portion and serve with skimmed milk from your daily allowance.

Variations: you can have 1 Fruit Selection with your muesli if you wish, but remember to deduct it from your daily allowance and your Selections remaining per day.

For 1 Fruit Selection choose from:
1 medium-size apple, chopped; or 1 medium-size pear, chopped; or 1 small banana, sliced.

For ¹/₂ Fruit Selection choose from:
¹/₂ oz (15 g) sultanas or raisins; or 1 oz (30 g) ready-to-eat dried apricots, prunes or dates, chopped; or 2 oz (60 g) seedless grapes.

Spiced Breakfast Fruits
Breakfast Muesli

Light Meals

In this chapter there are lots of exciting ideas for Light Meals which could be eaten either at lunchtime or in the evening, depending on when in the day you prefer to eat your Main Meal. Choose from warming soups, like Quick Minestrone (page 16) or Autumn Vegetable Soup (page 14), or easy one-pan recipes such as Spiced Prawns with Rice (page 20). There are some suggestions for salads too: try Mediterranean Tomatoes (page 18) or Chicken, Orange and Chick-pea Salad (page 18).

Whichever recipe you choose, you won't be disappointed. You'll be sticking to the Programme *and* giving your tastebuds a treat!

Hawaiian Toast Topper

Pineapple pieces are mixed with chopped ham and Cheddar cheese, and then spread on toast and grilled until bubbling, in this tasty Light Meal. The mixture makes a delicious sandwich filling, and can also be used as a stuffing for pitta bread.

Serves: 1

Calories per serving: 220

Preparation and cooking time: 10 minutes

Freezing: not recommended

Selections per serving: 1 Carbohydrate; 1 Fat;
1 Fruit; 1 Protein

Selections remaining per day: 3–5 Carbohydrate;
1–2 Fat; 1–2 Fruit; 2 Milk; 2–5 Protein;
3 Vegetable

2 pineapple rings (equal to 4 oz/120 g) in natural
juice, drained

¹/₂ oz (15 g) mature Cheddar cheese, grated

¹/₂ oz (15 g) cooked ham, chopped

2–3 drops of Tabasco sauce (optional)

1 oz (30 g) slice of brown or white bread

1 teaspoon margarine

1 Preheat the grill to hot. Chop one pineapple ring into small pieces and mix it with the grated cheese and ham. Add the Tabasco sauce, if using.

2 Toast the bread and spread it with the margarine. Spread the pineapple mixture over the toast and grill until it just begins to bubble on the surface. Place the remaining pineapple ring on top and grill for 1–2 minutes more.

3 Transfer to a warmed plate and serve at once with a mixed salad.

Optional for men and young people only: use an extra 1 oz (30 g) of cheese and spread the mixture on a 1 oz (30 g) slice of toast.

Autumn Vegetable Soup
Hawaiian Toast Topper

Autumn Vegetable Soup

This deliciously smooth soup is made from a selection of fresh seasonal vegetables. The lentils and low-fat soft cheese provide the protein.

Serves: 4

Calories per serving: 245

Preparation time: 25 minutes

Cooking time: 35 minutes

Freezing: recommended

Selections per serving: 1 Carbohydrate; 1 Fat; 1 Protein; 1½ Vegetable

Selections remaining per day: 3–5 Carbohydrate; 1–2 Fat; 2–3 Fruit; 2 Milk; 2–5 Protein; 1½ Vegetable

(V) if using vegetarian margarine and low-fat soft cheese

2 teaspoons olive or vegetable oil

2 teaspoons margarine

1 large onion, chopped

2 carrots, sliced

1 turnip, chopped

8 oz (240 g) parsnips, chopped

2 teaspoons paprika

½ teaspoon dried thyme

2 pints (1.2 litres) stock, made with 2 vegetable stock cubes

2 oz (60 g) red lentils

4 oz (120 g) low-fat soft cheese

salt and pepper

2 oz (60 g) thick-sliced white bread, cubed

1 Heat the oil and margarine together in a large saucepan. Add the onion, carrots, turnip and parsnips and sauté gently for 5–8 minutes. Stir in the paprika and thyme and cook gently for 1 minute more.

2 Add the stock and red lentils and bring to a boil; reduce the heat. Cover and simmer for 20–25 minutes, or until the vegetables are cooked.

3 Transfer the soup to a liquidiser or food processor and blend for 15–20 seconds, until smooth. Return to the saucepan and add the low-fat soft cheese, stirring to mix.

4 Heat very gently until almost boiling. Check the seasoning, adding salt and pepper to taste.

5 Toast the bread cubes, turning them often, to make croûtons. Serve the soup in warmed bowls and sprinkle on the croûtons, dividing them equally.

Variations: low-fat natural fromage frais makes a delicious alternative to the low-fat soft cheese.

Green or brown lentils can be substituted for the red variety, but they will take a little longer to cook.

Chicken and Chilli Beans

Twenty minutes is all it takes to prepare this dish from start to finish, so it's ideal for a quick lunch or supper for one. Just double the quantities for two!

Serves: 1

Calories per serving: 290

Preparation and cooking time: 20 minutes

Freezing: recommended

Selections per serving: 1 Carbohydrate; 1 Fat; 1 Protein; 3 Vegetable; 10 Optional Calories

Selections remaining per day: 3–5 Carbohydrate; 1–2 Fat; 2–3 Fruit; 2 Milk; 2–5 Protein

1 teaspoon vegetable oil

2 oz (60 g) skinless, boneless chicken breast, cubed

1 shallot or very small onion, chopped finely

2 oz (60 g) mushrooms, sliced

7 oz (210 g) canned chopped tomatoes

3 oz (90 g) canned red kidney beans, rinsed and drained

a pinch of dried mixed herbs

$1/_4$ teaspoon chilli powder

1 teaspoon paprika

salt and pepper

1 tablespoon low-fat natural yogurt, to serve

❶ Heat the oil in a saucepan and add the chicken. Cook over a high heat to seal and brown it on all sides.

❷ Add the shallot or onion and cook for 3–4 minutes more. Add the mushrooms, tomatoes, kidney beans, herbs, chilli powder and paprika. Bring it to a boil, stirring occasionally, and then cover the pan and reduce the heat. Simmer gently for 10 minutes, stirring from time to time.

❸ Check the seasoning and add salt and pepper to taste. Ladle on to a warmed serving plate, top with the low-fat natural yogurt and serve immediately.

Cook's note: if you're not keen on your food being too spicy, omit the chilli powder and use only the paprika, which has a milder taste.

Optional for men and young people only: increase the carbohydrate content by serving this with a 3 oz (90 g) portion of cooked long-grain rice. Add additional protein by allowing an extra 1 oz (30 g) of cooked chicken, or an extra 3 oz (90 g) of canned kidney beans.

Quick Minestrone Soup

A piping-hot bowl of soup is always warming and comforting – especially so when you are on a diet. Curl up on the sofa and savour every mouthful of this delicious Italian-inspired minestrone soup.

Serves: 4

Calories per serving: 245

Preparation time: 20 minutes

Cooking time: 20 minutes

Freezing: recommended

Selections per serving: 1 Carbohydrate; 1 Fat;
  1 Protein; 2 Vegetable

Selections remaining per day: 3–5 Carbohydrate;
  1–2 Fat; 2–3 Fruit; 2 Milk; 2–5 Protein;
  1 Vegetable

P if using vegetarian parmesan cheese and
margarine

2 teaspoons olive or vegetable oil

2 teaspoons margarine

1 large onion, chopped

2 garlic cloves, crushed

2 carrots, sliced

3 oz (90 g) green beans, sliced

14 oz (420 g) canned chopped tomatoes

1½ pints (900 ml) stock, made with 2 vegetable
  stock cubes

12 oz (360 g) canned mixed beans, rinsed and
  drained

2 oz (60 g) quick-cook spaghetti, broken into
  pieces

2 teaspoons dried mixed Italian herbs

salt and pepper

2 oz (60 g) grated parmesan cheese, to serve

❶ Heat the oil and margarine together in a large saucepan. Add the onion and garlic and sauté them gently for 5 minutes.

❷ Add the carrots, green beans, tomatoes, vegetable stock and beans. Bring to the boil, cover and reduce the heat. Simmer for 15–20 minutes.

❸ Add the spaghetti and herbs and cook for 5 minutes more, or until the spaghetti is cooked.

❹ Season to taste with salt and pepper. Serve, with ½ oz (15 g) of grated parmesan cheese per portion.

Variations: use any variety of canned beans that you like, such as red kidney beans, black-eyed beans, cannellini beans or even chick-peas.

Pasta shapes can be used instead of quick-cook spaghetti. Make sure they are cooked before you serve the soup. Most pasta shapes take 8–10 minutes to cook, although tiny 'soup' pasta shapes take only 3–4 minutes.

Quick Minestrone Soup
Chicken and Chilli Beans

Mediterranean Tomatoes

This quick and delicious tomato salad has a flavour of Italy, and tastes excellent with crusty french bread or warm ciabatta bread.

Serves: 1

Calories per serving: 260

Preparation time: 10 minutes + 15 minutes
standing

Freezing: not recommended

Selections per serving: 1 Carbohydrate; 1 Fat;
1 Protein; 2 Vegetable

Selections remaining per day: 3–5 Carbohydrate;
1–2 Fat; 2–3 Fruit; 2 Milk; 2–5 Protein;
1 Vegetable

1 teaspoon olive oil

1 teaspoon cider or white-wine vinegar

1 tablespoon lemon juice

2 teaspoons chopped fresh basil or parsley

1 small garlic clove, crushed (optional)

3 spring onions, chopped finely

3 tomatoes

1 oz (30 g) french or ciabatta bread

2 oz (60 g) ricotta or low-fat soft cheese

salt and pepper

(𝒱) if using vegetarian cheese

❶ In a small bowl, whisk together the olive oil, vinegar and lemon juice. Mix in the basil or parsley, garlic (if using) and spring onions. Season with salt and pepper.

❷ Slice the tomatoes and arrange them on a serving plate. Drizzle the dressing over them, and then cover the plate with clingfilm and leave to stand for 10–15 minutes, to absorb the flavour of the dressing.

❸ Slice the bread and spread it with the cheese. Serve with the tomatoes.

Cook's note: fresh plum tomatoes are delicious in this recipe, if you can get them, or look out for varieties that have been grown for their superior flavour.

Chicken, Orange and Chick-pea Salad

Choose this deliciously different salad when you're craving something a little out of the ordinary. The chick-peas, orange and mint give it a flavour of Morocco.

Serves: 1

Calories per serving: 255

Preparation time: 10 minutes

Freezing: not recommended

Selections per serving: 1 Carbohydrate; 1 Fat;
1 Fruit; 1 Protein; 2 Vegetable

Selections remaining per day: 3–5 Carbohydrate;
1–2 Fat; 1–2 Fruit; 2 Milk; 2–5 Protein;
1 Vegetable

1 teaspoon olive oil

1 teaspoon light malt vinegar

1 tablespoon finely chopped shallot or spring
onion

2 teaspoons chopped fresh mint or 1/2 teaspoon
dried mint

2-inch (5 cm) piece of cucumber, chopped

1 medium-size orange, segmented and chopped

3 oz (90 g) canned chick-peas, rinsed and drained

1 oz (30 g) cooked chicken, chopped

iceberg lettuce, shredded

salt and pepper

1 Combine the olive oil, vinegar, shallot or spring onion, and mint in a mixing bowl.

2 Add the cucumber, orange, chick-peas and chicken and mix well. Season to taste with salt and pepper.

3 Arrange a bed of shredded lettuce on a serving plate and pile the chicken mixture on top. Serve at once.

(V) **Vegetarian option:** substitute 2 oz (60 g) of smoked or firm tofu in place of the chicken. Leave the mixture to stand for a while before piling it on top of the lettuce, in order for the tofu to absorb the flavours of the other ingredients.

Spiced Prawns with Rice

Do you need something spicy to perk up a jaded palate? These prawns with a pinch of chilli and paprika will do the trick!

Serves: 1
Calories per serving: 235
Preparation and cooking time: 25 minutes
Freezing: not recommended
Selections per serving: 1 Carbohydrate; 1 Fat;
    1 Protein; 2 Vegetable
Selections remaining per day: 3–5 Carbohydrate;
    1–2 Fat; 2–3 Fruit; 2 Milk; 2–5 Protein;
    1 Vegetable

1 teaspoon vegetable oil
1 shallot or $1/2$ small onion, chopped finely
3 oz (90 g) button mushrooms
2 tomatoes, chopped
2 oz (60 g) frozen prawns, defrosted
3 oz (90 g) cooked long-grain rice
2 teaspoons chopped fresh parsley
1 teaspoon paprika
a pinch of chilli powder
salt and pepper

1 Heat the vegetable oil in a small frying-pan and sauté the shallot or onion for 3–4 minutes, until softened.

2 Add the mushrooms and tomatoes and continue to cook for 5 minutes more.

3 Stir in the prawns, cooked rice, parsley, paprika and chilli powder. Cook for 3–4 minutes more, stirring constantly, until heated through. Check the seasoning, adding salt and pepper and a little more chilli powder if necessary. Spoon on to a warmed plate and serve at once.

Variation: Drained, flaked tuna in brine can be used as alternatives to prawns.

Optional for men and young people only: increase the amount of prawns to 4 oz (120 g) and double the amount of cooked rice.

Previous page: Mediterranean Tomatoes
Chicken, Orange and Chick-pea Salad

This page: Spiced Prawns with Rice

Cauliflower with Ham, Cheese and Mustard Sauce

Vegetables are virtually unlimited on the Weight Watchers Programme, so you can really fill up on the cauliflower!
This delicious ham, cheese and mustard sauce makes it taste superb.

Serves: 1
Calories per serving: 270
Preparation and cooking time: 20 minutes
Freezing: not recommended
Selections per serving: $^1/_2$ Carbohydrate; $^1/_2$ Milk;
1 Protein; 3 Vegetable
Selections remaining per day: $3^1/_2$–$5^1/_2$
Carbohydrate; 2–3 Fat; 2–3 Fruit; $1^1/_2$ Milk;
2–5 Protein

10 oz (300 g) cauliflower, broken into florets
$^1/_4$ pint (150 ml) skimmed milk
$^1/_2$ oz (15 g) cornflour, mixed to a paste with a
little cold water
$^1/_2$ oz (15 g) cooked ham, chopped
$^1/_2$ oz (15 g) mature Cheddar cheese, grated
1 teaspoon whole-grain mustard
salt and pepper

❶ Cook the cauliflower in a saucepan with a small amount of boiling, lightly salted water until just tender.

❷ Lift the cauliflower on to a warm serving plate with a draining spoon and keep warm. Reserve the cooking liquid.

❸ Pour the milk into a measuring jug and add the cauliflower cooking liquid to bring the measure up to $^1/_2$ pint (300 ml); use extra water if necessary. Return the liquid to the saucepan and add the cornflour mixture. Heat, stirring constantly, until thickened and blended.

❹ Add the ham, cheese and mustard to the sauce and cook for about 30 seconds, stirring, until the cheese has melted. Season to taste with salt and pepper and pour over the cauliflower. Serve at once.

Variations: you can use $^1/_2$ oz (15 g) of grated parmesan cheese in place of the Cheddar cheese, if you wish, and substitute a pinch of dried mixed Italian herbs for the mustard.

(*✔*) **Vegetarian option:** substitute an extra $^1/_2$ oz (15 g) of cheese for the ham.

Cook's note: use a cheese with a strong flavour for the best results.

Weight Watchers note: Members following the Slim and Trim Programme should serve this meal with 1 slice of low-Calorie bread spread with 1 teaspoon of margarine. This will add $^1/_2$ Carbohydrate and 1 Fat Selection – remember to remove these from your Selections remaining.

Optional for men and young people only: add an extra 1 oz (30 g) of cheese or ham to increase the protein content.

Toasted Nut Pitta with Shredded Salad
Cauliflower with Ham, Cheese and Mustard Sauce
Tuna Cheese Bake

Toasted Nut Pitta with Shredded Salad

Lightly toasted nuts and seeds are combined with shredded cabbage, carrots, apple and cucumber, and then stuffed with feta cheese into warmed pitta bread in this unusual salad meal.

Serves: 1
Calories per serving: 300
Preparation time: 10 minutes
Freezing: not recommended
Selections per serving: 1 Carbohydrate; 1 Fat;
1 Fruit; 1 Protein; 1 Vegetable; 10 Optional Calories
Selections remaining per day: 3–5 Carbohydrate;
    1–2 Fat; 1–2 Fruit; 2 Milk; 2–5 Protein;
    2 Vegetable

(V) if using vegetarian feta cheese

¹/₂ oz (15 g) peanuts or pine kernels
1 oz (30 g) white cabbage, shredded
¹/₂ small carrot, grated
1-inch (2.5 cm) piece of cucumber, chopped finely
1 medium-size apple, cored and chopped
2 teaspoons lemon juice
1 tablespoon low-fat natural yogurt
1 oz (30 g) pitta bread
¹/₂ oz (15 g) feta cheese, cut in small cubes
salt and pepper

❶ Preheat the grill to medium. Scatter the nuts on to a baking sheet and grill them, turning occasionally, until light golden brown. Allow them to cool.
❷ Mix together the cabbage, carrot, cucumber and apple. Add the lemon juice, yogurt and nuts, stirring to combine. Season with salt and pepper.
❸ Warm the pitta bread and split it open. Stuff it with the nut salad and top it with the cubes of feta cheese.

Variation: you can use crisp lettuce instead of cabbage if you prefer, or try shredded chinese leaves.
Cook's note: feta cheese is quite salty, so go easy when seasoning the salad; add just a little salt.
Optional for men and young people only: serve 1 oz (30 g) of pitta bread and allow another 1 oz (30 g) of feta cheese.

Tuna Cheese Bake

A quick and tasty recipe always goes down a treat. This one combines rice and fresh vegetables with canned tuna, and is topped with breadcrumbs and grated cheese.

Serves: 1
Calories per serving: 265
Preparation time: 20 minutes
Cooking time: 20 minutes
Freezing: not recommended
Selections per serving: 1¹/₂ Carbohydrate; 1 Fat;
    1 Protein; 2 Vegetable
Selections remaining per day: 2¹/₂–4¹/₂
    Carbohydrate; 1–2 Fat; 2–3 Fruit; 2 Milk;
    2–5 Protein; 1 Vegetable

3 oz (90 g) dwarf green beans, sliced
1 tomato, cut in wedges
3 oz (90 g) cooked long-grain rice
1 oz (30 g) canned tuna in brine, drained
2 teaspoons lemon juice
1 teaspoon olive oil
1 teaspoon chopped fresh parsley
¹/₂ oz (15 g) fresh breadcrumbs
¹/₂ oz (15 g) Red Leicester cheese, grated
salt and pepper

❶ Preheat the oven to Gas Mark 5/190°C/375°F. Cook the green beans in a small amount of lightly salted boiling water for 5 minutes. Drain well.

❷ Mix together the dwarf green beans, tomato, cooked rice, tuna, lemon juice, olive oil and chopped fresh parsley. Season with some salt and pepper.

Transfer the mixture to an individual-size shallow baking dish.

❸ Mix together the breadcrumbs and cheese and sprinkle them over the rice mixture. Bake for 15–20 minutes, or until browned on the surface.

Variation: use any type of hard cheese instead of Red Leicester: Cheddar, Cheshire and Lancashire cheeses all work well.

Weight Watchers note: if you are very hungry, increase the amount of vegetables. You can add other varieties too, such as courgettes, peppers or mushrooms.

Puff-topped Vegetable Bake

Fresh vegetables are topped with triangles of bread soaked in egg and milk, in this nutritious Light Meal.

Serves: 1
Calories per serving: 250
Preparation time: 20 minutes
Cooking time: 20 minutes
Freezing: not recommended
Selections per serving: 1 Carbohydrate; 1 Fat;
   1 Protein; 3 Vegetable; 20 Optional Calories
Selections remaining per day: 3–5 Carbohydrate;
   1–2 Fat; 2–3 Fruit; 2 Milk; 2–5 Protein

(𝒫) if using free-range eggs and vegetarian margarine

1 oz (30 g) slice of bread, cut in triangles
1 small egg
2 tablespoons skimmed milk
1 courgette, sliced
1 celery stick, chopped finely
1 small leek, sliced
1/2 vegetable stock cube
1 teaspoon margarine
1 teaspoon grated parmesan cheese
salt and pepper

❶ Put the bread triangles in a shallow bowl. Beat the egg and milk together and pour this mixture over the bread. Leave to soak for 10–15 minutes. Preheat the oven to Gas Mark 5/190°C/375°F.

❷ Meanwhile, simmer the courgette, celery and leek in a small amount of water with the vegetable stock half-cube for 5–8 minutes, until the vegetables are lightly cooked. Drain well and discard the cooking liquid.

❸ Grease a small ovenproof baking dish with the margarine. Add the cooked vegetables and level the surface. Season with salt and pepper. Arrange the soaked bread triangles over the top, pouring over any remaining egg mixture. Sprinkle with parmesan cheese.

❹ Bake for 15–20 minutes, until puffed up and golden brown.

Cook's note: choose a small, deep baking dish in preference to a shallow one, so that the bread will cover the surface of the vegetables.

Weight Watchers note: use any selection and any amount of fresh vegetables as they are virtually unlimited.

Pasta with Pronto Sauce

Speed is of the essence with this tasty pasta recipe. It's an ideal Light Meal to make when you are so busy that you hardly have time to eat, let alone cook!

Serves: 1

Calories per serving: 240

Preparation and cooking time: 15 minutes

Freezing: not recommended

Selections per serving: 1 Carbohydrate; 1 Fat; 1 Protein; ½ Vegetable; 20 Optional Calories

Selections remaining per day: 3–5 Carbohydrate; 1–2 Fat; 2–3 Fruit; 2 Milk; 2–5 Protein; 2½ Vegetable

1 oz (30 g) pasta shapes

1 teaspoon margarine

3 spring onions, chopped finely

½ oz (15 g) cooked ham, chopped

1 oz (30 g) low-fat soft cheese

2 tablespoons skimmed milk

a pinch of dried mixed herbs

salt and pepper

1 teaspoon grated parmesan cheese, to serve

❶ Cook the pasta in plenty of boiling, lightly salted water for 8–10 minutes, until just tender.

❷ Meanwhile, melt the margarine in a small saucepan and sauté the spring onions for 3–4 minutes, until softened.

❸ Add the ham, low-fat soft cheese, milk and herbs, stirring to mix. Heat gently for 2 minutes.

❹ Drain the pasta, reserving 2 tablespoons of the cooking water. Add the pasta to the sauce with the reserved cooking water and stir to combine. Season to taste with salt and pepper.

❺ Sprinkle with the parmesan cheese and serve on a warmed plate.

Variation: as a substitute for the ham, use 1 oz (30 g) of defrosted frozen prawns or drained, flaked tuna fish in brine or water.

Optional for men and young people only: double the amount of pasta, ham and low-fat soft cheese used.

Puff-topped Vegetable Bake
Pasta with Pronto Sauce

Stuffed Jacket Potatoes

For a simple and satisfying Light Meal, you can't beat a jacket potato. There are three different filling suggestions here, so you can choose your favourite.

Serves: 4

Calories per serving: see individual fillings

Preparation time: 15 minutes

Cooking time: 1¼ hours

Freezing: not recommended

Selections per serving: 1 Carbohydrate; 1 Fat; 1 Protein; 1 Vegetable; 10 Optional Calories (the Spinach and blue cheese filling has no Optional Calories)

Selections remaining per day: 3–5 Carbohydrate; 1–2 Fat; 2–3 Fruit; 2 Milk; 2–5 Protein; 2 Vegetable

2 × 8 oz (240 g) potato

4 teaspoons margarine

salt and pepper

For the cheese and tomato filling

(270 Calories per serving including the potato):

4 oz (120 g) mature Cheddar cheese, grated

4 tomatoes, chopped

2 tablespoons plus 2 teaspoons tomato pickle

For the spinach and blue cheese filling

(255 Calories per serving including the potato):

9 oz (270 g) frozen spinach

4 oz (120 g) Danish blue or blue Stilton cheese, cubed

For the curried mushroom and bacon filling

(175 Calories per serving including the potato):

2 oz (60 g) lean back bacon

8 oz (240 g) mushrooms, wiped and sliced

¼ pint (150 ml) stock, made with ½ vegetable stock cube

2 teaspoons curry paste

❶ Preheat the oven to Gas Mark 6/200°C/400°F. Prick the potatoes with a fork and bake them for about an hour, until tender. Halve the potatoes, scoop out the insides, reserving the skins. Mix the cooked potato with the margarine, and then combine with one of the following filling mixtures.

❷ **Cheese and tomato filling:** mix together the cheese, tomatoes and tomato pickle with the potato until combined, seasoning with salt and pepper to taste.

Spinach and blue cheese filling: cook the spinach according to the package instructions. Drain it well and combine it with the cheese and potato, seasoning with salt and pepper to taste.

Curried mushroom and bacon filling: grill the bacon until crisp and then blot with kitchen paper before cutting it into small pieces. Simmer the mushrooms in the vegetable stock for 5 minutes. Drain them well, and then mix in the curry paste, bacon and potato. Season with salt and pepper to taste.

❸ Pack the potato skins with the filling mixture and return them to the oven for 10–15 minutes, to heat through. Serve hot, ½ potato per person.

Cook's notes: you can make just 2 servings by dividing the ingredients in half.

The potatoes can be microwaved on high for 6–8 minutes and then finished off in the oven once they are filled.

Main Meals

The recipe ideas in this chapter are simple, quick to prepare, healthy, and great tasting – what more could you ask for?

There are both savoury suggestions as well as ideas for desserts – something that you don't always expect to be offered by a weight-loss programme. These dessert ideas are healthy, supplying some protein, minerals and vitamins to your overall diet. So they are not simply pure indulgence, even though they may taste like it!

If you're following the Weight Watchers Programme, you can use these desserts as 'add-ons' to the Selections for your Main Meal, bringing your carbohydrate and protein allowances up to the higher limit, and making full use of your fruit allocation for that meal. So when you are still feeling hungry, and longing for something sweet to finish off your meal, these recipes can fit easily into your plan.

Remember that men and young people have a higher requirement for carbohydrate, protein and fruit, and many of the recipes suggest adjustments which will supply these extra Selections, without having to make radical alterations. Simple is best!

Poached Fish with Watercress Sauce

Poach a fillet of your favourite fish in some stock, and serve it with this quick and delicious watercress sauce.

Serves: 1
Calories per serving: 370
Preparation and cooking time: 25 minutes
Freezing: not recommended
Selections per serving: 2 Carbohydrate; 1 Fat;
   2 Protein; 1 Vegetable; 30 Optional Calories
Selections remaining per day: 2–4 Carbohydrate;
   1–2 Fat; 2–3 Fruit; 2 Milk; 1–4 Protein;
   2 Vegetable

8 oz (240 g) new potatoes
5 oz (150 g) fillet or cutlet of fish, e.g, hake, haddock, cod or coley
$1/3$ pint (200 ml) stock, made with $1/2$ fish or vegetable stock cube
a pinch of dried herbs
1 teaspoon margarine
1 shallot or 3 spring onions, chopped finely
1 oz (30 g) watercress, chopped very finely
2 tablespoons skimmed milk
2 teaspoons cornflour
salt and pepper

❶ Put the potatoes on to cook in plenty of boiling, lightly salted water.

❷ Rinse the fish and place it in a shallow pan with the stock and herbs. Cover it and cook it gently for 8–10 minutes, until the fish is opaque and the flesh flakes easily.

❸ Meanwhile, melt the margarine in a small saucepan and sauté the shallot or spring onions for about 5 minutes, until softened.

❹ Drain the poaching liquid from the fish and strain it into the saucepan with the margarine and onions. Keep the fish warm. Add the watercress to the saucepan and cook for 2 minutes. Blend the milk and cornflour together and stir them into the sauce. Heat, stirring constantly, until the sauce is thickened and smooth. Season with salt and pepper to taste.

❺ Drain the potatoes and serve them with the fish, accompanied by the watercress sauce.

Baked Stuffed Vegetables

Make a delicious cheesy filling to stuff fresh vegetables. Take your pick from whatever vegetables are at their seasonal best: marrows, courgettes, aubergines, large flat mushrooms and beef tomatoes are just a few of the varieties that you can use.

Serves: 1

Calories per serving: 540

Preparation time: 35 minutes

Cooking time: 25 minutes

Freezing: not recommended

Selections per serving: 2 Carbohydrate; 1 Fat;
2 Protein; 4 Vegetable

Selections remaining per day: 2–4 Carbohydrate;
1–2 Fat; 2–3 Fruit; 2 Milk; 1–4 Protein

(V) if using vegetarian Cheddar cheese

vegetables of your choice, for stuffing, e.g.,
2 × 3-inch (8 cm) slice of marrow, 2 medium-
size courgettes, 1 small aubergine, 2 large flat
mushrooms or 1 large beef tomato

salt and pepper

1 oz (30 g) crusty french bread, to serve

For the filling:

1 teaspoon olive oil

1 shallot or very small onion, chopped finely

1 small garlic clove, crushed (optional)

2 tomatoes, chopped

1¹/₂ oz (45 g) cooked long-grain rice

1¹/₂ oz (45 g) frozen sweetcorn kernels, thawed,
or canned, drained sweetcorn

¹/₂ teaspoon dried mixed herbs

2 oz (60 g) mature Cheddar cheese, grated

❶ Preheat the oven to Gas Mark 5/190°C/375°F. To make the filling, heat the olive oil in a small saucepan and sauté the shallot or onion and garlic (if using) for about 4–5 minutes, until softened.

❷ Add the tomatoes and cook until they are pulpy. Add the rice and sweetcorn. Stir in the herbs and the cheese and then remove from the heat. Season with salt and pepper to taste.

❸ Prepare the vegetables for stuffing. If using marrow or courgettes, scoop out the seeds and discard them. If using tomatoes, halve them, scoop out the seeds and add them to the filling. If using an

aubergine, halve it and scoop out the middle; then sprinkle the inside of each half liberally with salt, and leave for 10 minutes to extract the bitter juices. Rinse and pat them dry. If using mushrooms, remove the stalks, chop them finely and add them to the filling. Wipe the caps.

❹ Put the vegetables, hollow side up, into a baking dish and pack them with the filling. Cover with foil and bake for 20–25 minutes, or until cooked through. Remove the foil for the last 5 minutes of cooking time to brown the surface. Serve hot, with the bread.

Previous page: Poached Fish with Watercress Sauce
Baked Stuffed Vegetables

Spaghetti with Rich Tomato Bolognese Sauce

This is a delicious version of the classic Italian sauce, with lots of tomatoes and vegetables to fill you up without piling on the Calories.

Serves: 1
Calories per serving: 475
Preparation and cooking time: 45 minutes
Freezing: recommended
Selections per serving: 2 Carbohydrate; 1 Fat;
    2 Protein; 5 Vegetable; 10 Optional Calories
Selections remaining per day: 2–4 Carbohydrate;
    1–2 Fat; 2–3 Fruit; 2 Milk; 1–4 Protein

1 teaspoon olive or vegetable oil
1 very small onion, chopped finely
1 small garlic clove, crushed (optional)
1 celery stick, sliced
1 small carrot, sliced
7 oz (210 g) canned chopped tomatoes
3 oz (90 g) button mushrooms, wiped and sliced
1/2 teaspoon dried mixed Italian herbs
1 teaspoon tomato purée
3 oz (90 g) lean minced beef
2 oz (60 g) spaghetti or macaroni
salt and pepper
1 teaspoon parmesan cheese, to serve

1 Heat the oil in a medium-size saucepan and sauté the onion and garlic, if using, for 4–5 minutes, until softened.

2 Add the celery and carrot and cook, stirring, for 2 minutes more.

3 Pour the tomatoes into the saucepan and add the mushrooms, herbs and tomato purée. Stir well, and then bring to a boil. Cover and reduce the heat. Simmer gently for 10 minutes.

4 Meanwhile, form the minced beef into a patty shape and cook it under a hot grill, turning it once, until the fat stops dripping. Crumble the meat into the saucepan and cook, uncovered, for 10 minutes more.

5 Meanwhile, cook the spaghetti or macaroni in plenty of boiling, lightly salted water for about 6–8 minutes, until just tender.

6 Check the seasoning of the sauce, adding salt and pepper, according to taste. Drain the spaghetti or macaroni, place it on a warmed serving plate and top with the bolognese sauce. Sprinkle the parmesan cheese on top and serve at once.

(✓) **Vegetarian option:** substitute 4 oz (120 g) of minced Quorn for the minced beef, adding it to the sauce with the canned tomatoes.

Cook's note: if you're freezing this recipe, freeze the sauce only and cook the pasta just before serving.

Optional for men and young people only: cook an additional 1 oz (30 g) of spaghetti and add an extra 1 oz (30 g) of minced beef to the bolognese sauce.

Creamy Tuna Fish Pie

Chunks of tuna fish in a light cheese sauce with vegetables, topped with potato, makes a filling, tasty main-course dish.

Serves: 1

Calories per serving: 490

Preparation time: 30 minutes

Cooking time: 20 minutes

Freezing: recommended

Selections per serving: 2 Carbohydrate; 1 Fat; 1/2 Milk; 2 Protein; 2 Vegetable; 50 Optional Calories

Selections remaining per day: 2–4 Carbohydrate; 1–2 Fat; 2–3 Fruit; 1 1/2 Milk; 1–4 Protein; 1 Vegetable

8 oz (240 g) potatoes

1 small carrot, sliced

2 oz (60 g) broccoli or cauliflower, cut in small florets

1 teaspoon margarine

3 spring onions, chopped finely

1 tablespoon plain flour

1/3 pint (200 ml) skimmed milk

1/2 oz (15 g) mature Cheddar cheese, grated

3 oz (90 g) canned tuna fish in brine or water, drained

salt and pepper

❶ Preheat the oven to Gas Mark 6/200°C/400°F. Cook the potatoes in plenty of boiling, lightly salted water until just tender.

❷ Meanwhile, lightly cook the carrot and broccoli or cauliflower together: they should retain a little 'bite'.

❸ Melt the margarine in a small saucepan and add the spring onions. Sauté them for 3–4 minutes, until softened. Add the flour and cook gently for 1 minute, stirring. Remove from the heat.

❹ Gradually add the milk to the flour mixture, stirring to blend. Return to the heat and bring to a boil, stirring constantly, until thickened and smooth. Remove from the heat and add the grated cheese, allowing it to melt. Season with a little salt and pepper.

❺ Drain the carrot and broccoli or cauliflower and add them to the sauce, stirring to coat. Add the tuna

fish and stir it in lightly, to prevent it breaking up too much. Transfer to a small ovenproof baking dish. Drain and mash the potatoes, season them with a little salt and pepper, and spread them over the top of the tuna and vegetable mixture.

❻ Bake for 15–20 minutes. Serve hot.

Cook's notes: if you don't have time to finish the dish in the oven, just serve the tuna and vegetable mixture accompanied by the mashed potatoes.

To save yourself some washing up, you could microwave the vegetables, using the timings in your microwave instruction book.

Optional for men and young people only: increase the cheese to 1 1/2 oz (45 g) and the potatoes to 12 oz (240 g).

Spaghetti with Rich Tomato Bolognese Sauce
Creamy Tuna Fish Pie

Grilled Chicken with Mushroom Sauce

For a very tasty Main Meal, grill a small chicken breast, marinated in lemon and parsley, and then serve it with this creamy mushroom sauce. Pasta makes the perfect accompaniment.

Serves: 1

Calories per serving: 380

Preparation and cooking time: 1 hour marinating + 25 minutes

Freezing: not recommended

Selections per serving: 2 Carbohydrate; 1 Fat; 2 Protein; 1 Vegetable; 20 Optional Calories

Selections remaining per day: 2–4 Carbohydrate; 1–2 Fat; 2–3 Fruit; 2 Milk; 1–4 Protein; 2 Vegetable

3 oz (90 g) skinless, boneless chicken breast

2 tablespoons lemon juice

2 teaspoons finely chopped fresh parsley

1 small garlic clove, crushed (optional)

1 teaspoon olive or vegetable oil

2 oz (60 g) pasta shapes

3 oz (90 g) button mushrooms, sliced

1/3 pint (200 ml) stock, made with 1/2 vegetable stock cube

2 teaspoons cornflour, blended with a little water

salt and pepper

❶ Split the chicken breast in half horizontally, without cutting it right through. Open it out flat and lay it in a shallow dish. Mix together the lemon juice, parsley, garlic (if using) and oil. Season with salt and pepper and pour the marinade over the chicken. Cover with clingfilm and allow to marinate for one hour, turning once.

❷ Preheat the grill and cook the chicken for about 12 minutes, turning it once, and basting it often with the marinade. Put the pasta on to cook in plenty of boiling, lightly salted water.

❸ Whilst the chicken and pasta are cooking, put the mushrooms into a saucepan with the vegetable stock. Bring to a boil, reduce the heat and simmer gently for 5 minutes.

❹ Add the blended cornflour to the mushrooms and heat, stirring constantly, until thickened and smooth.

❺ Drain the pasta and spoon it on to a warmed plate. Serve the chicken and pour over the mushroom sauce.

Cook's note: substitute fresh basil, oregano, marjoram or chives in place of the parsley, if you prefer.

Weight Watchers note: if you are very hungry, cook yourself some extra vegetables – carrots or broccoli would be perfect with this dish.

Optional for men and young people only: increase the Carbohydrate and Protein Selections by adding an extra 1 oz (30 g) to both the pasta and chicken.

Grilled Chicken with Mushroom Sauce
Mile-high Stir-fry

Mile-high Stir-fry

Remember you can eat up to 1½ lb (720 g) of vegetables each day, so you really can pile your plate a mile high.

Serves: 1

Calories per serving: 405

Preparation and cooking time: 25 minutes

Freezing: not recommended

Selections per serving: 2 Carbohydrate; 1 Fat; 2 Protein; 5 Vegetable

Selections remaining per day: 2–4 Carbohydrate; 1–2 Fat; 2-3 Fruit; 2 Milk; 1–4 Protein

1 oz (30 g) long-grain rice

1 teaspoon sesame or vegetable oil

3 oz (90 g) skinless, boneless chicken breast, cut in thin strips

4 spring onions, sliced

1 small carrot, cut in matchsticks

½ small red pepper, deseeded and cut in matchsticks

3 oz (90 g) cauliflower or broccoli, cut in small florets

3 oz (90 g) dwarf green beans or mangetout

3 oz (90 g) baby corn

2 teaspoons light soy sauce

salt and pepper

❶ Cook the rice in plenty of boiling, lightly salted water for about 12 minutes, until just tender.

❷ Meanwhile, prepare the stir-fry. Heat the oil in a wok or frying-pan and add the chicken, stir-frying it over a high heat for 2–3 minutes, until the strips are sealed on all sides.

❸ Add all the vegetables and stir-fry them for 4–5 minutes, until they are cooked yet still crunchy.

❹ Season the stir-fry with the soy sauce and some salt and pepper. Pile it on to a warmed plate and serve it with the drained, cooked rice.

Variations: instead of chicken, use 3 oz (90 g) of turkey, or 6 oz (180 g) of firm white fish or prawns.

(V) **Vegetarian option:** 4 oz (120 g) of smoked or firm tofu, or Quorn can be used in place of the chicken.

Cook's note: for extra flavour, add ½ teaspoon of five-spice powder to the stir-fry when seasoning with the salt and pepper.

Optional for men and young people only: cook an extra 1 oz (30 g) of rice and increase the chicken (or equivalent) to 4 oz (120 g).

Chinese Chicken and Noodles

This is an easy recipe for an oriental-style soupy-stew. Its Chinese character comes from the egg-noodles, soy sauce and five-spice powder. Although it has quite a long list of ingredients, it doesn't take long to prepare.

Serves: 1

Calories per serving: 460

Preparation and cooking time: 35 minutes

Freezing: not recommended

Selections per serving: 2 Carbohydrate; 1 Fat; 2 Protein; 3 Vegetable

Selections remaining per day: 2–4 Carbohydrate; 1–2 Fat; 2–3 Fruit; 2 Milk; 1–4 Protein

1 teaspoon sesame or vegetable oil

1 shallot or 4 spring onions, chopped

1 celery stick, sliced

1/2 pint (300 ml) stock, made with a vegetable stock cube

3 oz (90 g) boneless, skinless chicken, cut in fine strips

1 small carrot, cut in matchsticks

2 oz (60 g) oyster mushrooms or button mushrooms

2 oz (60 g) chinese leaves or white cabbage, shredded

1/2 teaspoon five-spice powder

2 teaspoons light soy sauce

2 oz (60 g) thread egg-noodles

salt and pepper

❶ Heat the oil in a medium-size saucepan and sauté the shallot or spring onions and celery for 4–5 minutes, or until softened.

❷ Add the vegetable stock, chicken and carrot. Bring to a boil, and then reduce the heat and simmer gently for 15 minutes or until the chicken is cooked through.

❸ Add the mushrooms, chinese leaves or cabbage, five-spice powder, soy sauce and egg-noodles. Cook gently, stirring occasionally, for 5 minutes more. Season with salt and pepper to taste and serve at once, ladled into a warmed bowl.

(✓) **Vegetarian option:** substitute 4 oz (120 g) of Quorn cubes or smoked tofu for the chicken.

Sweet and Sour Beef and Peppers

*Lots of fresh vegetables and some tender rump steak make a quick and colourful main-course meal. Vary the vegetables
as you like; for example, if you're not keen on peppers, substitute mangetout, mushrooms or courgettes.*

Serves: 1

Calories per serving: 480

Preparation and cooking time: 25 minutes

Freezing: not recommended

Selections per serving: 2 Carbohydrate; 1 Fat;
2 Protein; 4 Vegetable; 50 Optional Calories

Selections remaining per day: 2–4 Carbohydrate;
1–2 Fat; 2–3 Fruit; 2 Milk; 1–4 Protein

2 oz (60 g) long-grain rice

1 tablespoon white-wine vinegar

1 tablespoon medium sherry

1 tablespoon light soy sauce

1 teaspoon molasses sugar

1 teaspoon cornflour

1 teaspoon vegetable oil

3 oz (90 g) lean rump steak, sliced finely

1 small carrot, cut in fine strips

2-inch (5 cm) piece of cucumber, cut in fine strips

**1/2 small red pepper, cored, deseeded and cut into
fine strips**

**1/2 small yellow pepper, cored, deseeded and cut
into fine strips**

a pinch of ground ginger

a pinch of ground allspice

salt and pepper

❶ Cook the rice in plenty of boiling, lightly salted
water for about 12 minutes, or until tender.

❷ Meanwhile, make the sweet and sour sauce. Put
the vinegar, sherry, soy sauce, sugar and cornflour in
a small saucepan and heat them gently, stirring, until
the sauce is thickened and smooth. Remove from
the heat.

❸ Heat the oil in a frying-pan or wok and add the
steak. Stir-fry over a high heat for 3–4 minutes.

❹ Add all the vegetables and stir-fry them for

3–4 minutes more. Add the ginger, allspice and
sweet and sour sauce, stirring to mix. Heat through
for 2 minutes. Check the seasoning, adding salt and
pepper to taste.

❺ Drain the rice and spoon it on to a warmed plate,
with the stir-fry. Serve at once.

Cook's note: cucumber tastes particularly good
when stir-fried, although you may think it is a little
unusual. Substitute a small onion or 4 or 5 spring
onions, sliced finely, if you prefer.

*Sweet and Sour Beef and Peppers
Chinese Chicken and Noodles
Vegetable Risotto*

Vegetable Risotto

Creamy risotto is always delicious. This is a vegetarian version, using pine kernels and cheese for protein and flavour. Make it with inexpensive, everyday vegetables – as in this recipe – or make it more special with asparagus, mangetout and oyster mushrooms.

Serves: 1

Preparation and cooking time: 45 minutes

Calories per serving: 560

Freezing: not recommended

Selections per serving: 2 Carbohydrate; 1 Fat;
2 Protein; 2 Vegetable; 60 Optional Calories

Selections remaining per day: 2–4 Carbohydrate;
1–2 Fat; 2–3 Fruit; 2 Milk; 1–4 Protein;
1 Vegetable

Ⓥ if using vegetarian Cheddar cheese

1 teaspoon olive oil

2 oz (60 g) risotto or long-grain rice

1 very small onion, chopped finely

2 oz (60 g) mushrooms, wiped and sliced

1/2 small green or red pepper, de-seeded and chopped

2 teaspoons pine kernels

1/2 pint (300 ml) stock, made with 1/2 vegetable stock cube

2 oz (60 g) mature Cheddar cheese, grated

2 teaspoons chopped fresh herbs, e.g., parsley, thyme, oregano or basil, or 1 teaspoon dried herbs

salt and pepper

❶ Heat the oil in a frying-pan. Add the rice and sauté it without browning, for 5 minutes. Add the onion, mushrooms, pepper and pine kernels and sauté for 5 minutes more.

❷ Pour in the stock and bring it to a boil. Reduce the heat and simmer over a low heat for 12–15 minutes, stirring often, until the rice is tender and the liquid has been absorbed. The risotto should have a creamy texture.

❸ Add the cheese and herbs to the risotto and stir through until just melted. Season with salt and pepper to taste. Spoon on to a warmed plate and serve at once.

Cook's note: if the liquid has evaporated before the rice is cooked properly, add a little extra water and continue cooking until the rice is tender.

Pancakes with Lemon and Orange Sauce

Make yourself a dessert that is nutritious, and not something that just adds on empty Calories. Pancakes fit the bill perfectly, because they provide protein, carbohydrate and calcium from the egg, flour and milk.

Serves: 4

Calories per serving: 220

Preparation and cooking time: 15 minutes

Freezing: recommended

Selections per serving: 1 Carbohydrate; ¹/₂ Fat;
   1 Fruit; ¹/₄ Milk; 25 Optional Calories

Selections remaining per day: 3–5 Carbohydrate;
   1¹/₂–2¹/₂ Fat; 1–2 Fruit; 1³/₄ Milk; 3–6 Protein;
   3 Vegetable

(P) if using a free-range egg

4 oz (120 g) plain flour

a pinch of salt

1 egg

¹/₂ pint (300 ml) skimmed milk

2 teaspoons vegetable oil

juice of 1 lemon

8 fl oz (240 ml) unsweetened orange juice

4 teaspoons cornflour

**2 medium-size oranges, peeled, pith removed
   and sliced into segments**

artificial sweetener, to taste

❶ In a large bowl, whisk together the flour, salt, egg and milk to make a thin batter. It should be about the same consistency as single cream.

❷ Heat a small, heavy-based frying-pan and add 2–3 drops of oil. Spoon about 2 tablespoons of batter into the pan to make a thin pancake. Tilt the pan to swirl the batter evenly over the base.

❸ Cook the pancake over a medium heat until the top is set and bubbles rise to the pancake's surface. Gently flip it over to cook the other side. Cook 8 pancakes in this way, fold them into triangles and put them in a baking dish. Cover with foil and keep them warm in a low oven.

❹ To make the sauce, put the lemon juice, orange juice and cornflour into a small saucepan and whisk together to blend. Heat, stirring constantly, until thickened and smooth. Add the oranges and a little artificial sweetener to taste. Cook gently for 1 minute.

❺ Pour the hot sauce over the pancakes and serve two per person.

Cook's note: this dish may be frozen complete, although it is nicer to freeze only the pancakes and to make the sauce fresh before serving.

Raspberry Baked Custard

Serves: 1
Calories per serving: 225
Preparation time: 5 minutes
Cooking time: 35 minutes
Freezing: not recommended
Selections per serving: 1 Fruit; 1/2 Milk; 1 Protein; 50 Optional Calories
Selections remaining per day: 4–6 Carbohydrate; 2–3 Fat; 1–2 Fruit; 1 1/2 Milk; 2–5 Protein; 3 Vegetable

V if using a free-range egg

1 egg
1/4 pint (150 ml) skimmed milk
3–4 drops of vanilla essence
2 1/2 teaspoons caster sugar
4 oz (120 g) fresh or frozen raspberries

❶ Preheat the oven to Gas Mark 4/180°C/350°F.
❷ Beat together the egg, milk, vanilla essence and sugar to make a custard.
❸ Put the raspberries into a small, deep ovenproof baking dish or ramekin and pour over the custard.
❹ Stand the dish in a small roasting tin, and pour in enough warm water to reach half-way up the side of the baking dish. Bake for 30–35 minutes, or until set. Serve warm or chilled.

Variations: apples, blackberries, or frozen forest fruits could be used instead of raspberries.

Cook's note: baking the custard in a roasting tin of warm water, or 'bain-marie', gives a more even temperature and a smoother consistency.

Chocolate Bread Pudding

Serves: 1
Calories per serving: 255
Preparation time: 10 minutes + 2 hours soaking
Cooking time: 35 minutes
Freezing: not recommended
Selections per serving: 1 Carbohydrate; 1/2 Milk; 1 Protein; 50 Optional Calories
Selections remaining per day: 3–5 Carbohydrate; 2–3 Fat; 2-3 Fruit; 1 1/2 Milk; 2–5 Protein; 3 Vegetable

V if using a free-range egg

1 oz (30 g) bread, cubed
2 teaspoons unsweetened cocoa powder, dissolved in 2 tablespoons hot water
1/4 pint (150 ml) skimmed milk
1 egg
2 teaspoons caster sugar
3–4 drops of vanilla essence

❶ Put the bread cubes into a small ovenproof baking dish.
❷ Beat together the cocoa mixture, milk, egg, sugar and vanilla essence. Pour this carefully over the bread. Cover the dish with clingfilm and refrigerate it for 2 hours, or overnight if preferred.
❸ Preheat the oven to Gas Mark 4/180°C/350°F. Remove the clingfilm and bake the pudding for 30–35 minutes, or until set. Serve hot.

Variations: if you like the idea of a Coffee Bread Pudding, substitute 2 teaspoons of instant coffee for the cocoa powder, dissolving it in a little hot water in the same way. This will reduce the Optional Calories to 40.

Cook's note: this recipe provides quite a substantial portion – you may just want to eat half of it and save the rest for later. If covered, it can be refrigerated for up to 2 days.

Apple and Apricot Cheese Whip

Make the most of some of the fruit that you eat as part of the Programme by transforming it into this light and lovely dessert.

Serves: 1

Calories per serving: 115

Preparation and cooking time: 20 minutes + chilling

Freezing: not recommended

Selections per serving: 1½ Fruit; 1 Protein;

Selections remaining per day: 4–6 Carbohydrate;
2–3 Fat; ½–1½ Fruit; 2 Milk; 2–5 Protein;
3 Vegetable

Ⓥ if using vegetarian low-fat soft cheese

1 medium-size apple

2 teaspoons lemon juice

½ oz (15 g) ready-to-eat dried apricots, chopped

3 fl oz (90 ml) water

artificial sweetener, to taste

2 oz (60 g) low-fat soft cheese or low-fat
fromage frais

❶ Peel, core and roughly chop the apple. Reserve some of the peel for decoration, dipping it in the lemon juice to prevent it turning brown. Reserve a quarter of a dried apricot for decoration.

❷ Put the apple and remaining apricots in a small saucepan, with the water. Cook gently until the apple is tender, about 10 minutes. Allow to cool.

❸ Purée the fruit mixture in a blender or food processor, or push it through a sieve, or mash it with a fork. Sweeten to taste with a little artificial sweetener, if required. Transfer half of it to a small serving glass.

❹ Beat the low-fat soft cheese or fromage frais in a bowl to soften it, and then stir in the remaining fruit. Spoon the mixture into the serving glass.

❺ Cut the reserved apple peel and apricot into fine strips and decorate the dessert. Serve chilled.

Variation: in summer, you could use fresh berries instead of apples and apricots. Raspberries and strawberries would make a delicious combination. There is no need to cook these fruits first, so omit the water.

Previous page: Pancakes with Lemon and Orange Sauce
Raspberry Baked Custard

This page: Apple and Apricot Cheese Whip
Chocolate Bread Pudding